MATA, MAMA
& ME

BY
SWAMINI SUPRIYANANDA

C·H·I·N·M·A·Y·A   B·A·L·A   K·A·T·H·A

DEVI MATA IS
THE MOTHER OF THE WHOLE WORLD

SHE LOOKS AFTER
THE SUN, EARTH,
WATER...
AND EVERYONE

DEVI MATA
MADE THE SUN

My MAMA
WAKES ME UP

DEVI MATA
MADE WATER

MY MAMA
GIVES ME A BATH

DEVI MATA
MADE
THE EARTH,
FRUITS AND
VEGETABLES

My MAMA
FEEDS ME

DEVI MATA IS KNOWLEDGE

My MAMA
TEACHES ME

DEVI MATA
IS WEALTH

My MAMA
LOOKS AFTER MY NEEDS

DEVI MATA
IS STRENGTH

My Mama...
MAKES ME STRONG

DEVI MATA
MADE
THE MOON

My MAMA
SINGS ME
TO SLEEP

DEVI MATA
IS EVERYONE'S MAMA

DEVI MATA
LOVES EVERYONE

JUST LIKE
MY MAMA LOVES ME